better latté than never

knife & packer

it's grim up north london
the popular cartoon
strip from **PRIVATE EYE**

FLICK HERE AND SEE!!

These cartoon strips originally appeared in PRIVATE EYE
Published in Great Britain by
Private Eye Productions Ltd, 6 Carlisle Street, London W1D 3BN

© 2001 Knife and Packer

ISBN 1 901784 23 1

Designed by Bridget Tisdall

Printed in England by Ebenezer Baylis & Son Ltd, Worcester

2 4 6 8 10 9 7 5 3 1

better latté than never

knife & packer

it's grim up north london
the popular cartoon strip from **PRIVATE EYE**

HOW WE MET }}

Jez Paterson & Quin Lovis

"that particular morning the brioche meant more to me than a simple brunch accompaniment"

}} **Jez:** People are always drawn together in a time of crisis and Quin and I were no exception. . .

Quin: Yes, when I first met Jez I was struck by his selflessness and courage in the face of imminent calamity. . .

Jez: It was just another Sunday brunch and I was at my usual window seat in Rodolphe's (at the time the only place serving a decent Eggs Benedict outside of the Left Bank) when it was announced to me that there was a crisis in the kitchen. . .

Quin: . . . it turned out that we had both ordered the last savoury brioche and Rodolphe was having kittens. . . finally he called us both over to plead 'mano a mano' who should have the last pastry. . .

Jez: I explained to Quin that that particular morning the brioche meant more to me than a simple brunch accompaniment. I described the ordeal of having discovered, only hours earlier, that the decorators had completely wrecked my roof terrace by unwittingly concreting over the Umbrian terracotta flagstones. . .

Quin: I'd recently gone through a similar experience when an irresponsible landscape gardener had botched a Moorish water feature I had had especially imported stone by stone from Andalucia. . . so I felt his pain. . .

Jez: In the end we both settled for the *tarte aux fraises* and before you could say 'N1' we were on a cycling holiday in Provence. ■

1. BEANS
Arabica is the bean most used in the coffee boutiques and as a result it should be avoided at all costs. We favour the more exotic fruity bean and the pungent Panamanian Black is our current pick of the crop.

2. GRINDING
Electric grinders detract from the flavour. We opt for the more artisan approach of hand-beating the beans with mallets (preferably fashioned by Costa Rican Indians in their native teak).

3. FROTHING
A crucial part in the making of a presentable cappuccino. A good test is whether your froth can support the weight of an organic grape.

4. EMBELLISHING
Man has sprinkled his cappuccino since time immemorial. Chocolate and cinnamon are frankly outmoded and we have never looked back since discovering the joy of adorning our hot beverages with macadamia shavings.

5. PRESENTING
Cup, mug, glass? The debate rages. However even an average cappuccino can be rescued by a sufficiently exquisite item of crockery.

6. AND FINALLY
Add friends and a smattering of intellectual debate. *BLISS.*

THE WORLD OF

ARTS FESTIVALS 1

Later in WORLD OF ARTS FESTIVALS II
Jez and Quin tread the boards in
their very own production

BRIAN LOVIS: Quin's always been a fussy eater – he simply would not eat tinned baby food. In fact, his first word was "organic". He was always a rebellious child whose tantrums were legendary. I'll never forget his 7th birthday, which we were celebrating at a Berni Inn in Bournemouth. Quin spent twenty-five minutes lecturing the chef on the correct consistency of a crème caramel. I've never seen a grown man cry like that, before or since. ■

DEIRDRE PATERSON:
Jez always knew his own mind from an early age and took a lively interest in soft furnishings. Before Jez was born my husband, Malcolm, spent months preparing a nursery for our eagerly awaited firstborn. Snazzy pictures of the Banana Splits, the Clangers and the Wombles adorned the walls. But all this was swept away when Jez discovered stencilling and the more muted colours of the Mediterranean hacienda. Nothing's changed really and he still gets on my back about the layout of my Lilliput figurine collection. ■

A LIFE IN THE DAY OF FENELLA FOLSTROP

Fenella Folstrup, 33, is a freelance war photographer who has taken pictures in some of the most dangerous places in the world. When not overseas she resides in north London with her two cats Darkroom and Zoom

Waking up in a war zone: the air is filled with the plaintive cry of women and children and the screeching of shells and mortars and I always ask myself the same question: *'Where am I going to get a decent pain au chocolat?'*.

Then it's off to the battle zone. People often ask me what is the worst thing about war and I always say, the smell. It's a unique smell, indescribable,

beyond human understanding: it's the smell of lousy frontline coffee. Due to some absurd red tape the UN won't allow us to have cafetières.

At the end of a long day I like to 'give a little back' to whichever community I happen to be staying in. I always make for the local hospital to give succour to the injured. It breaks my heart to see such ill-equipped hospitals. Most don't even have an aromatherapist on site and have the bare minimum of essential oils.

And as I go to sleep, drained and having given so much of myself, I wonder, *'Why? Why? Why? Why can't they airlift in a decent patisserie chef?'*

LOVIS
FOR LONDON

VOTE QUIN LOVIS FOR LONDON MAYOR

May 4th 2000

Those Lovis Promises In Full

1. An Espresso machine in every classroom.

2. Tax breaks for designer shops in all London boroughs.

3. Fashion guru Paul Smith to be appointed 'Tube Czar' (with special remit to update uniforms and improve carriage interiors).

Join Team Lovis Now!

 # THE WORLD OF

ARTS FESTIVALS II

FIN

QUIN AND JEZ 'DRESS TO IMPRESS'

Quin's Office Attire

ROLL NECK SWEATER Move over collar and tie, I've seen the future and it's roll neck. Smart but functional you can't expect to be taken seriously in a new media office without one.

LEATHER JACKET What does this say about you when you walk into the office? It says: 'Get out of my face, man, I've got a dot com business to run!'

PEDAL PUSHERS With a top half that reeks of business my bottom half cocks a snook to upper echelon management. Pedal Pushers show that you've got shins and you're proud of them.

SANDALS You never know the ups and downs your career might present to you and sandals are the 4 x 4's of the footwear world. Whether I'm checking out a new graphics package or chilling by the company pool table I know they won't let me down.

Jez's Street Wear

EYEWEAR Even if you have 20/20 vision, glasses or 'facial furniture' are a must if you want to turn heads.

GOATEE How often has an unkempt goatee ruined that all important first impression – I trim mine daily. And there's nothing worse than 'froth snaggling', an occupational hazard for the cappuccino-drinking goatee wearer.

URBAN SATCHELETTE The shoulder bag you're simply naked without... The mobile phone pocket has been the biggest technological break-through since steam.

MULTI-POCKETED UTILITY TROUSER More than a trouser, they're a way of life. How did our forefathers manage with only two pockets?

grim baby

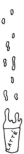

Pass
notes

North London

So where is it? It's in the name, dummy... but basically it's anywhere that's not south of the river.

What's so special about it? Wake up and smell the latté! It shakes and bakes, man. In fact it's got more shake than a Gulf state and more bake than a French patisserie chef.

So all you do is party and eat cakes, then? Get out of it... we keep the country running.

How exactly do you do that? By running dot com businesses and interior designing... without North London you'd never have had a 70s beige dentist's chair in every loft apartment.

So you all live in lofts? No. Some of us live in exquisitely renovated Georgian terraces.

They must cost a few bob? Yes. Next question…

So how old is North London? Old. Some places have had coffee machines since the early 70s!

Ah, steamed coffee drinks – the North London staff of life. Look, mate, don't get fresh with us…

Or what? Er… must dash, my scooter's on a double yellow! Ciao! ■

In Conversation...

Islington Celebrity Chef: Tinto Ranzotti

Quin: So, Tinto, if you had one ingredient you simply couldn't do without what would it be?

Tinto: I defy anyone to run a decent kitchen without a ready supply of Lebanese chickpeas – free trade, of course. They get overlooked time and time and time again. They work as a starter, as a main and even as a pudding.

Quin: Yes – your Chickpea Brulée is to die for!!!

Tinto: It's never off the menu.

Jez: What about leftovers? Any recipes for those annoying remnants lurking in the darker recesses of the fridge?

Tinto: What have you got?

Quin: We're at absolute rock bottom – half a roast quail, a free range mackerel, a pound of vegan gorgonzola and an organic aubergine.

Tinto: Simplicity itself! Quail and mackerel lasagne.

Jez and Quin: BRILLIANT!!!

Quin: So how would you round off a meal? Coffee versus liqueur

Tinto: Neither

Jez and Quinn: *(gasp)*

Tinto: No, really. Every meal should be rounded off with Breton oysters. There's nothing better at breaking down proteins and carbohydrates.

Jez and Quin: Bless!

GRIM EXTREME SPORTS

**Forget free-style rock climbing! Lose high-altitude paragliding!
Here in North London we really take it to the max!!!**

CHAI-DIVING

This high octane extreme sport requires a cool nerve and a steady hand as the 'Chai-Diver' mixes exotic teas in the same cup. Anything goes as radical 'herbals' such as Jamaican Orchid and Eucalyptus are infused with'traditionals' such as Darjeeling and Lapsang Suchong – with complete disregard for personal safety.

CHEESE BOARDING

Cheese as the final course of a meal?!?!
No way José if you're a Cheeseboarder – these wild dudes not only rip up the form book, they then throw it out the window. Often eschewing protective clothing, hard and soft cheeses alike are consumed with scant regard to old style *fromage* etiquette at any time of the day or night.

WHITE WATER DRINKING

This extreme sport pushes its protagonists to the outer reaches of human endurance. Completely uninsured and at their own risk, these mavericks think nothing of hitting the taps and drinking the water. H_2O boy!

GRUNGEE JUMPING

For hardcore adrenalin junkees only! Training to the peak of physical fitness, Grungee Jumpers search the streets for people wearing this terrifyingly outmoded fashion. Upon spotting a grunge wearing Kurt Cobain wannabee the Grungee Jumper quite literally 'jumps' out of the way. This is high stakes stuff as any sort of contact could result in a 'style meltdown' – potentially leading to dreadlocks.